# All Kinds of Mothers

# ALL KINDS OF

# MOTHERS

by CECILY BROWNSTONE
pictures by MIRIAM BROFSKY

David McKay Company, Inc.

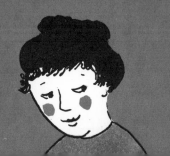

*for*

*Alexander Brofsky*

# A Message to Mothers

In this unusual and rhythmic little book, Cecily Brownstone has given approval, distinction, and charm to all kinds of mothers. You and your children will realize, as together you read her book, that there are many differences between mothers and that they do not always stay the same. How monotonous if they did!

Mothers are accustomed to reading to their children about other mother–people — Mother Goose, the Old Lady Who Lived in a Shoe, witches, and queens. In *All Kinds of Mothers,* a mother reads about herself and about other real mothers. Her child is given the chance to realize that mothers vary, and that he can be glad his mother is who she is.

This book can be of help in several ways. First, the child who hears his mother read it aloud will not only enjoy the rhythm and pictures, but will also absorb a mother's recognition of herself as a unique person with a variety of characteristics.

Second, the child who can read the book himself will speculate and philosophize about his mother as well as about himself as a unique person. He will find a mixture of simple words pleasantly fitted together along with some interesting longer ones that will stimulate his curiosity to learn as well as to appreciate different appearances and combinations in books and in people.

And last, mothers, seeing themselves portrayed as individuals, will have the way paved for them to see their children as individuals. They will then appreciate, rather than be concerned, about the many variations in their children. Some will be tall, some short; some will love to help with household chores, some will not; some will be dancers and some mechanics. Each one can fill a role, be loved, and respected.

*— Florence L. Swanson, M.D.*
Medical Director,
Montclair Child Guidance Center
Montclair, New Jersey

There are all kinds of mothers in the world.
They come in different shapes and sizes.

Some mothers are tall.
Some mothers are short.

Some mothers are nice and roly-poly.
Some mothers are nice and slim.

And some mothers are soft and furry.

Does your mother feel
nice and roly-poly?
nice and slim?

Which mother is soft and furry?

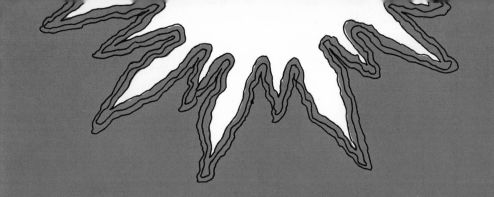

**Mothers come in different colors.**

Some mothers are light.
Some mothers are dark.

Some mothers like to sit in the sun and toast.

**Some mothers have short hair.**
**Some mothers have long hair.**

Some mothers have curlytops . . . like little lambs.
Some mothers' hair is absolutely straight . . . like
ponytails.

Some mothers have wavy hair . . . like the ocean.

Is your mother's hair . . .
    short?
    long?
    curly?
    absolutely straight?
    wavy like the ocean?

**All mothers wish their children would behave** most of the time. But even when children are naughty and do things their mothers don't like, *mothers keep right on loving them.*

**Some mothers really like to cook.**

They cook miles and miles of spaghetti
and loads and loads of meatballs.

**Some mothers are short-order cooks.**

They bake cakes out of boxes
and heat up TV dinners.

Does your mother ever give you . . .

spaghetti?
meat balls?
chocolate?
cake?
popcorn?

ice cream?
spinach?
carrots?
soup?
apples?

**There are noisy mothers and quiet mothers.**

Noisy mothers talk in a big loud voice. Sometimes they make funny, noisy things happen. Quiet mothers talk in a small quiet voice. Both noisy mothers and quiet mothers talk in a very special voice when they tell you a secret. Sometimes children whisper secrets to their mothers.

Do *you* have a secret to whisper?

# Some mothers are neat and tidy.

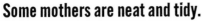

They usually want toys
to be straightened up.

## Some mothers are a little messy.

They don't mind if sometimes
toys are in a jumble.

All mothers like children to put toys away
*all by themselves*. But sometimes mothers
say, "Come on, I'll help you put
your toys away."

# Where do you like to put your toys away . . .

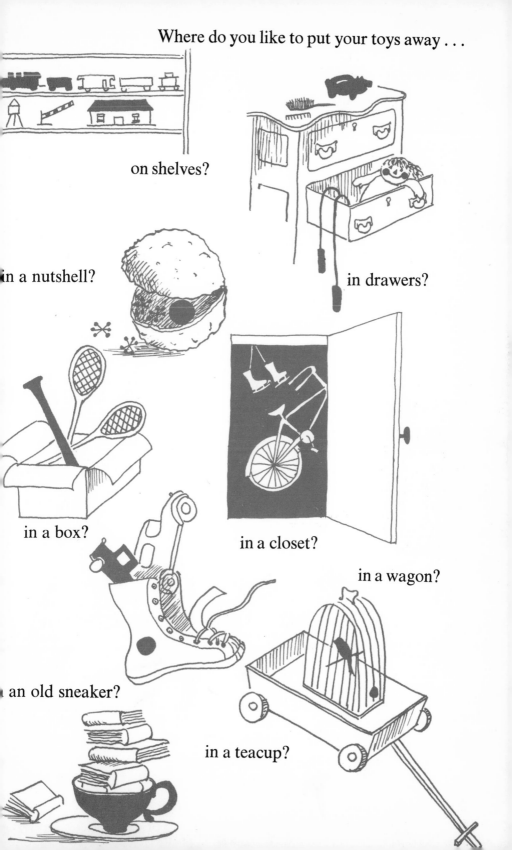

on shelves?

in drawers?

in a nutshell?

in a box?

in a closet?

in a wagon?

an old sneaker?

in a teacup?

**Some mothers talk a long long time on the telephone.**

Children get tired of waiting for mothers
       while they talk
              and talk
                     and talk . . .

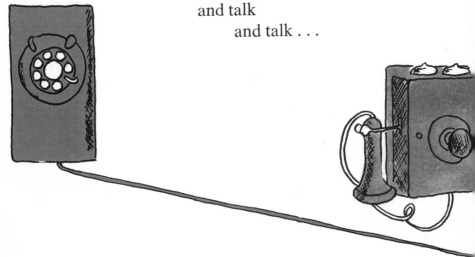

**Some mothers call**

the butcher to say,
       "Send me some meat;"

the grocer to say,
   "Send me some honey;"

the department store to say,
   "Send me some tiny little candles for
   my child's great big birthday cake!"

**Some mothers like to go places.**

They take their children to a farm
to see the chickens scratch, watch the
ducks waddle, hear the turkeys gobble.

**Some mothers like to go for walks.**

They wait while their children stop
to watch the fire engine zoom, pick up
a pebble, turn over a stone, or
jump down one step.

Would you like your mother to take you to a . . .

supermarket?

chocolate factory?

farm?

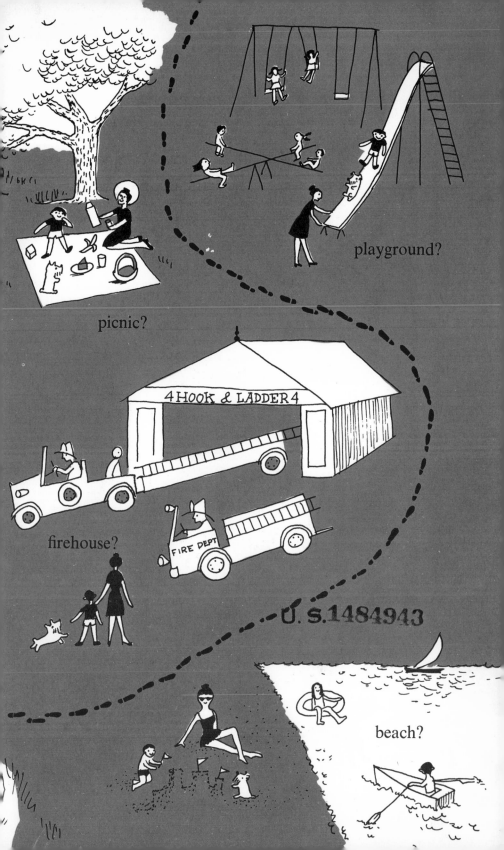

playground?

picnic?

4 HOOK & LADDER 4

FIRE DEPT

firehouse?

U.S.1484943

beach?

**Some mothers**

take their children to the zoo

to hear the seals bark.

**Some mothers stay at home and work.**

They cook, do the dishes, vacuum the house, wash and iron. Sometimes they do a little carpentering, sewing, or typing. Sometimes they practice dancing or music-playing, or they paint pictures or make sculptures. Sometimes their children help them.

**Some mothers go to work almost every day.**

They come home in the afternoon or at suppertime.
They work in bakeries, canneries, factories, groceries,
laboratories . . . beautoriums, eatoriums, emporiums
. . . schools, offices, libraries, and some other places.

**Some mothers doze the winter away.**

**Some mothers are sleepyheads.**

In the morning they open
one eye and say, "Tell Daddy
to give you breakfast."

**Some mothers like to get up early.**

They jump right out of bed, get dressed, putthecereal-inthebowl, putthebreadinthe toaster, cooktheeggs-andbacon, getoutthejamandjellyandpeanutbutter, makethepancakes and say, "Let's all have a *good* breakfast!"

Are you ever a sleepyhead?

**All mothers like to tuck their children in at bedtime.**

Some mothers say, "Sweet dreams!"
Some mothers say, "See you tomorrow!"

Would you like to tuck your mother in?

Some mothers love a great many people,
some mothers love just a few.
But no matter how many people or how few people
*your* mother loves, she has pitchers
 and *pitchers*
  and PITCHERS of love
   just for YOU.